ART OF COLORING

30 IMAGES TO INSPIRE CREATIVITY

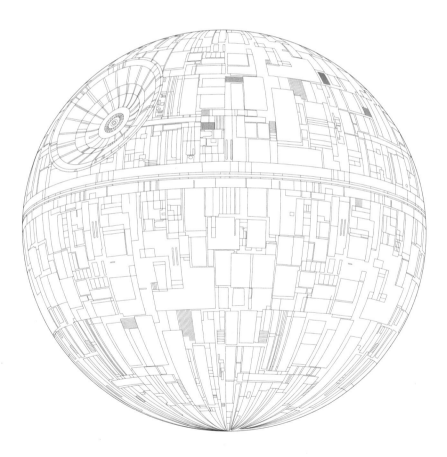

Disney
LUCASFILM
PRESS

Los Angeles · New York

All rights reserved. Published by Disney • Lucasfilm Press, an imprint of Disney Book Group.
No part of this book may be reproduced or transmitted in any form or by any means,
electronic or mechanical, including photocopying, recording, or by any information storage and
retrieval system, without written permission from the publisher.
For information address Disney • Lucasfilm Press, 1101 Flower Street, Glendale, California 91201.
Printed in the United States of America
First Edition, May 2017
1 3 5 7 9 10 8 6 4 2
ISBN 978-1-368-01518-9
FAC-014353-17110

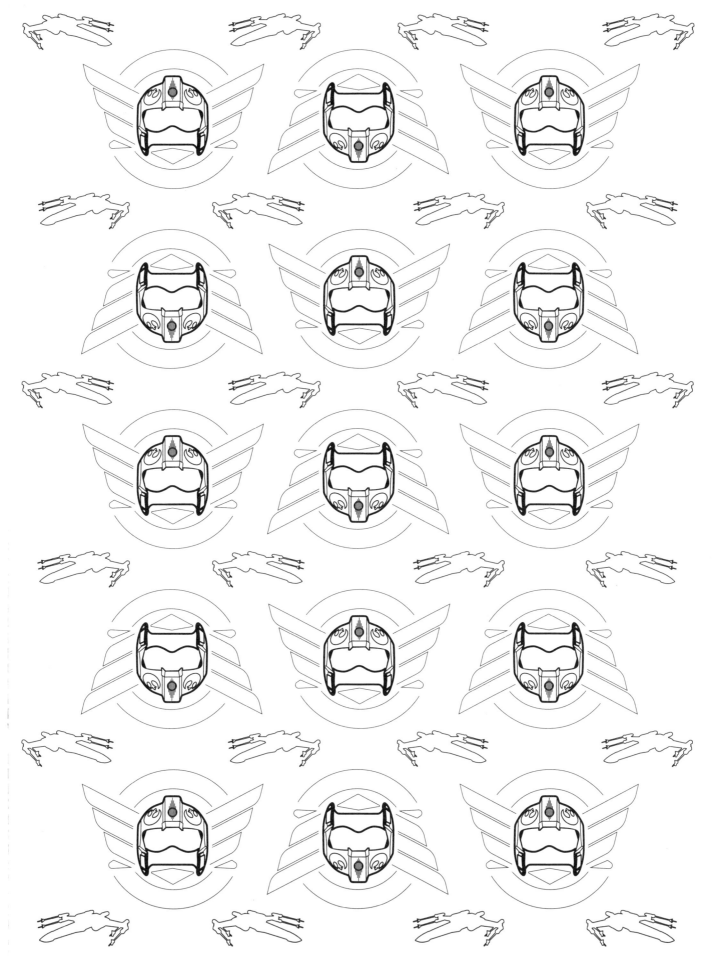

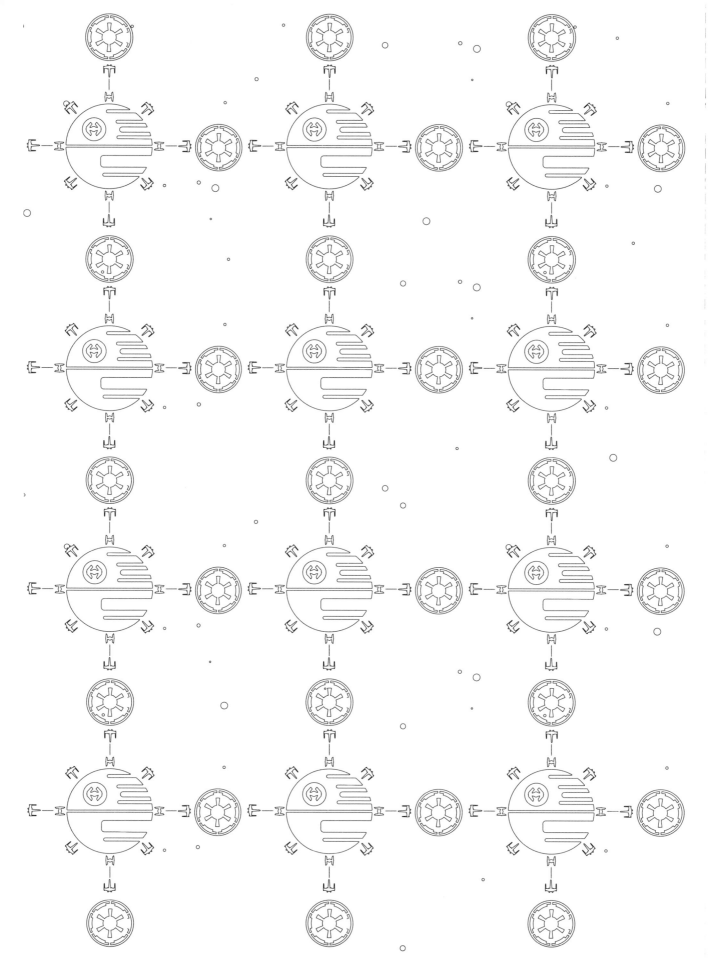

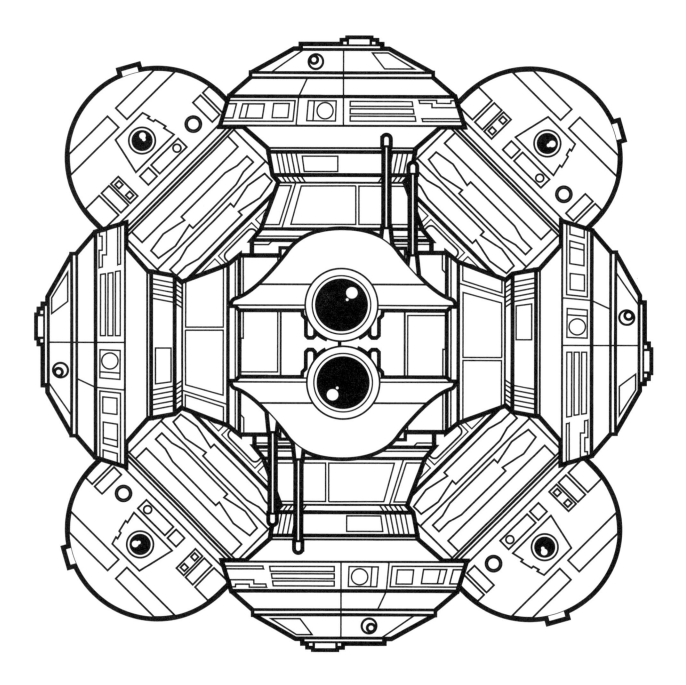

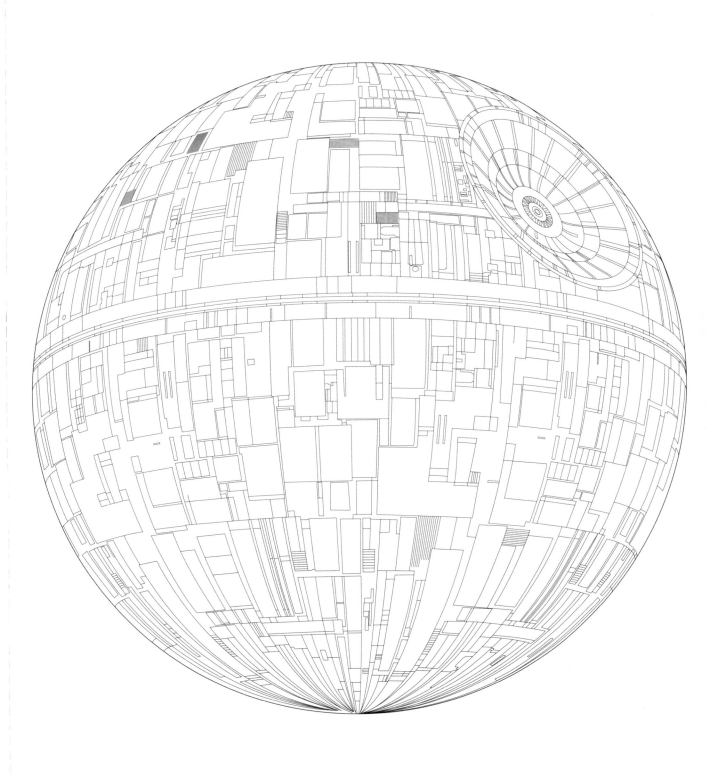

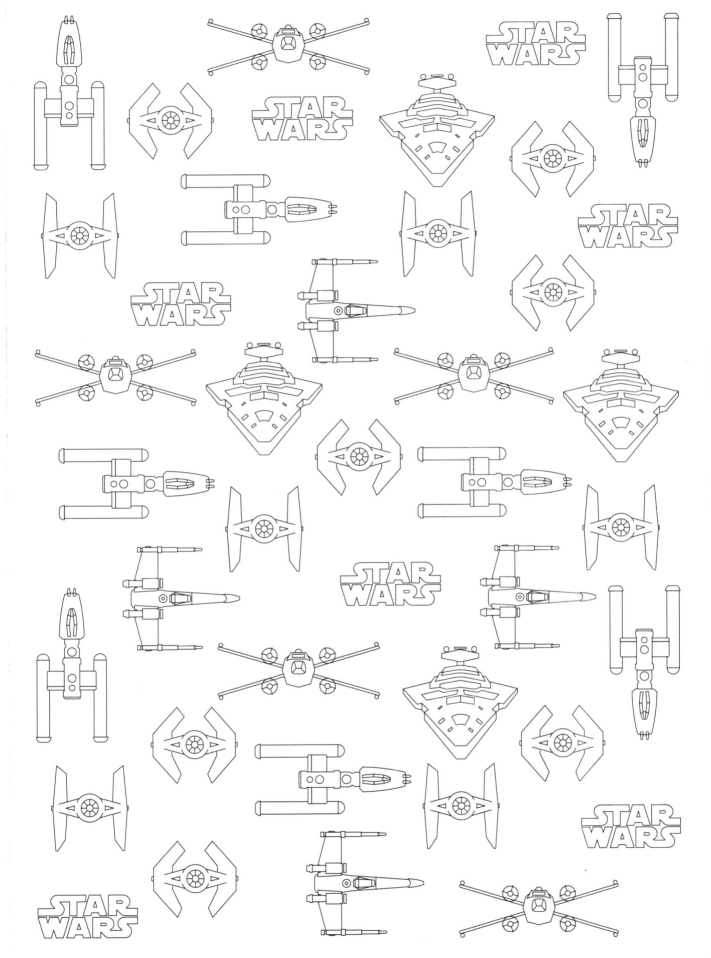

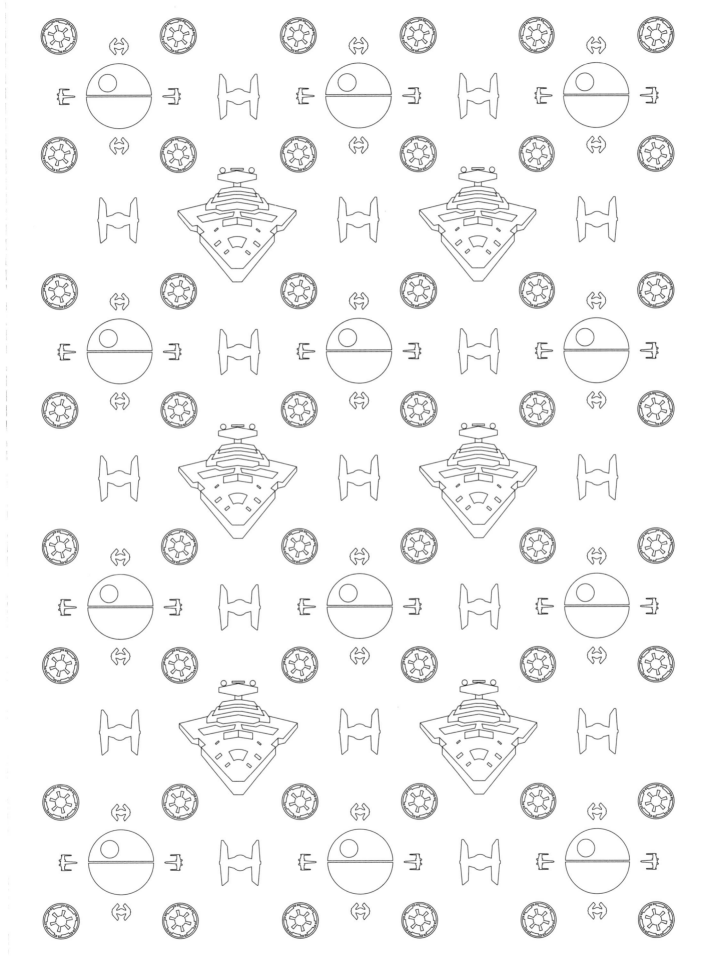